MAGIC MAGUIRE

and The Happy Hat

Written by Glynnis Maguire

Illustrated by Becca Hall

I dedicate this book to you, the reader.

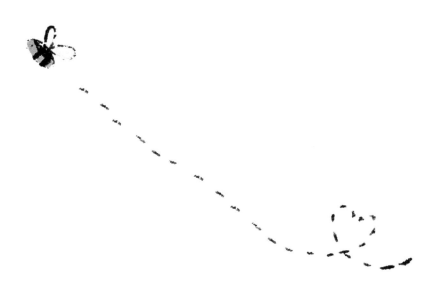

Dear Lovely Reader,

Thank you so much for choosing this book. Although it is little, it is powerful.

Magic Maguire is a meditation star and will help your child learn that it's okay to be who they are, to find a connection to themselves and know that life can be whatever they want it to be.

In order for your child to benefit the most, you will need to believe this too. Raising children is wonderful, wild and worrisome.

Meditation allows you to connect to yourself, to know your own heart and to live life from that place. Remember, the most important person to nurture and to love is you! Every person is unique and you are enough just the way you are.

When you love and nurture yourself, you're able to love and nurture others in the most authentic way. Self-nurturing is the best gift you will ever give to yourself, and – guess what? – you truly deserve it. The most helpful way to do this is to connect to your breath.

Remember to 'be' a little more and to 'do' a little less.

Magic Maguire's magic words are 'Whizz Woooo'. 'Whizz' the sound the breath makes as you inhale and 'Woooo' the sound as you exhale. As you practise your breath meditation, use these words. You can then teach your child to use them too.

Encourage your child to follow Magic's actions. This will help their energy to settle and will allow them to enjoy the moment. Stay present and you will begin to notice what is best for your child.

B R E A T H meditation

Sit or stand.

Allow the body to relax.

Close your eyes if you feel the need.

Be aware of your feet planted firmly on the ground.

Take a deep breath in through the nose if possible. If not, it's fine to take the breath through the mouth: 'Whizz'.

Allow the breath to travel into the body.

No need to strain; just be comfortable.

Place one hand on your heart, the other on your stomach.

Notice how you feel.

Let the breath release slowly through the nostrils or the mouth: 'Woooo'.

Tune into the movement of the body with the breath. Feel your feet on the ground.

Continue with more of the same; even deepen the breath. Notice how you feel.

Woooo...

Have a little shrug of the shoulders.

Repeat often during your day and most definitely when reading this book.

Remember, when you feel this calm connection to yourself, you will communicate with your child in the most beautiful and rewarding way.

A little message for new nurturers

Although your baby bundle is tiny, you can most definitely include them in your meditation.

As you breathe, notice your feet on the ground.

Imagine that the ground is sending beautiful, loving energy through the soles of the feet.

With each breath, feel this energy filling the whole of your body, particularly around your heart.

Visualise sending this energy from your heart and wrapping it carefully around your baby.

You can picture this energy as a colour; pink and green are associated with love and the heart.

Happy Connecting

Hello, my name is Magic Maguire and I have special powers.

I love
the stars
and the moon,

I love a nap
in the afternoon.

I love the sun
and the sea,

But most of all I love me.

Magic is ace – so are you.

It's time to find your 'Whizz Woooo'.

Do please practise every day,

'I AM ME'

you're proud to say.

Breathe in:

'WHIZZ'

Whizz . . .

Let the air
tickle your nose,

Feel a tingling
in your toes.

Let your tummy
fill with air,

See
a big
balloon
in
there.

Breathe out:

'WOOOO'

Woooo...

Let the air
tickle your nose,

Feel a tingling
in your toes.

Let the big
balloon go flat,

Smile and wear
your Happy Hat.

Always find time to
love you,

And remember your

'WHIZZ'

'WOOOO'

These moments will make sure that

you care for your

HAPPY HAT.

Dear Lovely Reader,

Thank you for taking the time to share this book.

The most important gifts that you can give your child are love, respect, time and the ability to find their own balance.

So, well done you! You're doing an amazing job! Give yourself a huge pat on the back.

If you've enjoyed this little book, please do watch out for Magic Maguire's next guide: *Magic Maguire and the Floaty Feather.*

There isn't a right way or a wrong way to practise meditation; it's simply whatever feels right for you. Allow yourself the time to 'go quiet'. Find your breath, tune into your heart and the rest will follow. 'Whizz Woooo' your way through the wonderful, wild and worrisome moments.

Keep wearing your Happy Hat and encourage your child to wear theirs.

Happy Nurturing

The End

or is it just the beginning?

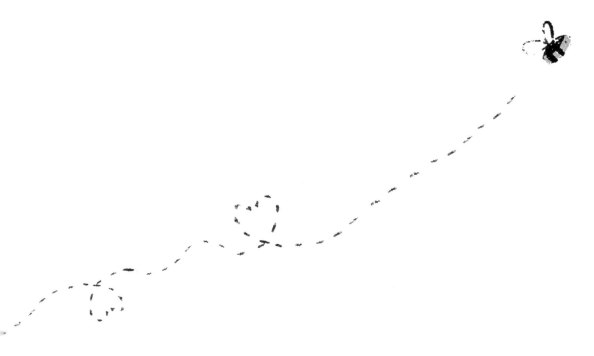

Matador
9 Priory Business Park
Wistow Road, Kibworth Beauchamp
Leicestershire, LE8 0RX
Tel: 0116 2792299
Email: books@troubador.co.uk
Web: www.troubador.co.uk/matador
Twitter: @matadorbooks

ISBN 978 1789016 932

British Library Cataloguing in Publication Data.
A catalogue record for this book is available from the British Library.

Printed and bound by CPI Group (UK) Ltd, Croydon, CR0 4YY
Typeset in 20pt Josefin Sans by Troubador Publishing Ltd, Leicester, UK

Matador is an imprint of Troubador Publishing Ltd

Please do visit www.adoveslife.co.uk for more meditation help.